CW00406876

STAR MATHS TOOLS

Interactive
maths made easy

TERMS AND CONDITIONS

IMPORTANT – PERMITTED USE AND WARNINGS – READ CAREFULLY BEFORE USING

Minimum specification:
- PC or Mac with a CD-ROM drive and at least 512 Mb RAM (recommended)
- Recommended screen resolution: 1280 × 1024 pixels (see CD-ROM help notes for details)
- Facilities for printing

PC:
- Windows 98SE or above
- Recommended minimum processor speed: 1 GHz

Mac:
- Mac OSX.4 or above
- Recommended minimum processor speed: 1 GHz

For all technical support queries, please phone Scholastic Customer Services on 0845 6039091.

Anthony David and Julie Cogill

Authors
Anthony David and Julie Cogill

Anthony David dedicates this book to his wife, Peachey, and sons Oliver and Samuel.

Digital Resource Design & Development
Vivid Interactive

Development Editors
Robin Hunt and Niamh O'Carroll

Editors
Christine Vaughan and Nicola Morgan

Assistant Editor
Margaret Eaton

Series Designers
Joy Monkhouse and Melissa Leeke

Designer
Quadrum Solutions Pvt. Ltd.

Text © 2009 Anthony David and Julie Cogill
© 2009 Scholastic Ltd

Tools © Vivid Interactive Ltd 2009

Designed using Adobe CS

Published by Scholastic Ltd
Villiers House, Clarendon Avenue,
Leamington Spa, Warwickshire CV32 5PR
www.scholastic.co.uk

Printed by Tien Wah, Singapore
1 2 3 4 5 6 7 8 9   9 0 1 2 3 4 5 6 7 8

ISBN 978-1407-10197-2

ACKNOWLEDGEMENTS
Extracts from the Primary National Strategy's *Primary Framework for Mathematics* (2006)
www.standards.dfes.gov.uk/primaryframework © Crown copyright. Reproduced under the terms of the
Click Use Licence.

The approved SMART Software Accreditation logo is a trademark of SMART Technologies.

Coin designs are covered by Crown copyright.

Every effort has been made to trace copyright holders for the works reproduced in this book, and the
publishers apologise for any inadvertent omissions.

British Library Cataloguing-in-Publication Data
A catalogue record for this book is available from the British Library.

Introduction

In the CPD programme, *Guide for your professional development: Using ICT to support mathematics in primary schools,* the DfES identified the following as important for teachers in determining whether to use ICT in primary mathematics:

- ICT should enhance good mathematics teaching. It should be used in lessons only if it supports good practice in teaching mathematics.
- Any decision about using ICT in a particular lesson (or sequence of lessons) must be directly related to the teaching and learning objectives for those lessons.
- ICT should be used if the teacher and/or the children can achieve something more effectively with it than without it.

Careful consideration and planning are therefore needed to fulfil the potential of the full range of ICT. HMI have since reported that, although ICT is increasingly available in schools, its effectiveness and appropriate use is variable with too many programs failing to support the teaching and learning of a specific learning objective and often used just for the sake of it!

Using ICT as a demonstration and modelling tool with the whole class is, however, a particularly effective use of technology. The *Star Maths Tools* series is designed to provide classes and teachers with a stimulating bank of interactive resources that can be used to demonstrate and model maths teaching, as well as to explore specific mathematical ideas, concepts and objectives.

About Star Maths Tools

Star Maths Tools is a new series of books with accompanying CD-ROMs that offers teachers a set of highly configurable maths tools for use across the primary maths curriculum. The ten tools on each CD-ROM are accessible to all teachers (however confident they might be in using whiteboard tools) and are designed to:

- provide potential for all children to be actively involved in teaching and learning
- provide potential for teachers to structure and manage interactive maths teaching for a variety of purposes across the maths curriculum.

Each tool in each year group is fully configurable to cover all ability levels. The accompanying teachers' notes also reflect differentiation and progression across a range of PNS renewed Framework objectives. The *Star Maths Tools* will enable teachers to develop a rich bank of teaching activities that fit into their existing planning framework and that can be used to support a range of learning objectives within each year group.

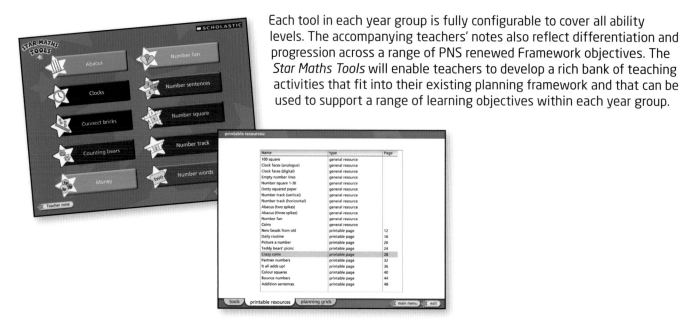

About the book

Each book includes a bank of teachers' notes linked to each of the *Star Maths Tools* on the CD-ROM. A photocopiable resource sheet is also provided for each tool to help to reinforce concepts which have been demonstrated or modelled using the tools.

Objectives grid

The planning grid on pages 7–8 provides a comprehensive guide identifying the links in each of the activities to the *Primary Framework for Mathematics* strands and objectives. Text highlighted in blue indicates the end-of-year objectives for the different strands.

Activity pages

A four-page teaching unit is provided for each of the ten tools in the following format:

About the tool

The first page of each unit includes annotated screen shots containing at-a-glance instructions for using the tool. Notes on key tool functions and a brief overview of the possible uses of each tool are also provided.

Activity notes

The second and third pages of each teaching unit include four specific teaching activities. Each activity includes the following notes:

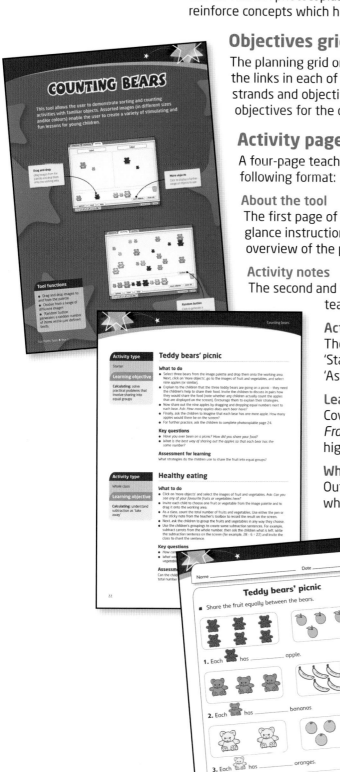

Activity type

The teaching covers a range of different purposes including 'Starter', 'Whole class', 'Review', 'Paired', 'Group' and 'Assessment' activities.

Learning objective

Covering the strands and objectives of the renewed *Primary Framework for Mathematics*. End-of-year objectives are highlighted in blue.

What to do

Outline notes on how to administer the activity with the whole class, groups, pairs and so on.

Key questions

Probing questions to be used during the activity.

Assessment for learning

Key assessment points and criteria for assessing each activity.

Activity resource sheet

The fourth page of each teaching unit is a photocopiable resource sheet (also available in printable format on the CD-ROM). These resource sheets are designed to provide outlines of the tools for recording purposes or to consolidate or extend learning.

About the CD-ROM

The CD-ROM includes the following ten tools:

Abacus	Clocks	Connect bricks	Counting bears	Money

Number fan	Number sentences	Number square	Number track	Number words
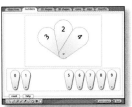				

Objectives screen

The opening screen of each of the ten tools offers teachers the opportunity to type in their own lesson objective.

Teacher's toolbox

All of the activities on the CD-ROM feature a set of interactive whiteboard tools, which include a pen tool, a highlighter tool, a line tool and a notepad for the teacher or child at the board to write questions, answers and a record of workings-out.

Teacher zone

The teachers' section includes links from the tools activities to the *Primary Framework for Mathematics* strands, together with an editable objectives grid provided in Word format, a diary page and printable versions of the worksheets. A selection of general resource sheets for recording work away from the whiteboard or PC is also included.

How to use the CD-ROM

System requirements

Minimum specification
- PC with a CD-ROM drive and 512 Mb RAM (recommended)
- Windows 98SE or above/Mac OSX.4 or above
- Recommended minimum processor speed: 1 GHz

Getting started

The *Star Maths Tools* CD-ROM should auto run when inserted into your CD drive. If it does not, browse to your CD drive to view the contents of the CD-ROM and click on the *Star Maths Tools* icon.

From the start-up screen you will find four options: select **Credits** to view a list of acknowledgements. Click on **Register** to register the product in order to receive product updates and special offers. Click on **How to use** to access support notes for using the CD-ROM. Finally, if you agree to the terms and conditions, select **Start** to move to the main menu.

For all technical support queries, please contact Scholastic Customer Services help desk on 0845 6039091.

Tool	Page No.	Activity title	Learning objective
Abacus	10	Grab the beads	**Knowing and using number facts:** count on or back in ones and tens
		Going down	**Calculating:** understand subtraction as 'take away'
	11	Big numbers	**Calculating:** use practical and informal written methods to support the addition of a one-digit number or a multiple of 10 to a one-digit or two-digit number
		New beads from old	**Knowing and using number facts:** count on or back in tens
Clocks	14	Daily routine	**Measuring:** read the time to the hour and half-hour
		Ding dong!	**Measuring:** read the time to the hour
	15	Time challenge	**Counting and understanding number:** say the number that is 1 more or less than any given number
		Tell the time	**Measuring:** read the time to the hour and half-hour
Connect bricks	18	Sharing strawberries	**Calculating:** solve practical problems that involve sharing into equal groups
		Mix the bricks	**Calculating:** count reliably, recognising that when rearranged the number of objects stays the same
	19	Picture a number	**Calculating:** use the vocabulary related to addition and symbols to describe and record addition number sentences
		Grab three	**Using and applying mathematics:** describe simple patterns and relationships involving numbers
Counting bears	22	Teddy bears' picnic	**Calculating:** solve practical problems that involve sharing into equal groups
		Healthy eating	**Calculating:** understand subtraction as 'take away'
	23	What a mix-up!	**Counting and understanding number:** count reliably at least 20 objects, recognising that when rearranged the number of objects stays the same
		How many?	**Counting and understanding number:** estimate a number of objects that can be checked by counting
Money	26	Penny chews	**Using and applying mathematics:** solve problems involving counting money, for example to 'pay' and 'give change'
		A big problem!	**Using and applying mathematics:** solve problems involving money
	27	Crazy coins	**Using and applying mathematics:** solve problems involving adding money
		Money towers	**Counting and understanding number:** compare and order numbers

Tool	Page No.	Activity title	Learning objective
Number fan	30	What shape is it?	**Understanding shape:** visualise and name common 2D shapes and describe their features
		Forwards and backwards	**Knowing and using number facts:** count on or back in ones
	31	Partner numbers	**Knowing and using number facts:** derive and recall addition facts for totals to at least 5
		Mixed months	**Measuring:** order months
Number sentences	34	One more/one less	**Counting and understanding number:** say the number that is 1 more or less than any given number
		Finger on/finger off	**Knowing and using number facts:** count on or back in ones, twos, fives and tens
	35	Mystery sentence	**Calculating:** use the vocabulary related to addition and subtraction and symbols to describe and record addition and subtraction number sentences
		Double up	**Knowing and using number facts:** recall the doubles of all numbers to at least 10
Number square	38	Match multiples	**Knowing and using number facts:** count on or back in ones, twos, fives and tens and use this knowledge to derive the multiples of 2, 5 and 10 to the tenth multiple
		What's ahead and what's behind?	**Calculating:** relate addition to counting on
	39	Colour squares	**Using and applying mathematics:** describe simple patterns and relationships involving numbers
		Joining numbers	**Calculating:** find a 'difference' by counting up
Number track	42	Up and down numbers	**Knowing and using number facts:** count on or back in ones, twos, fives and tens
		Fill the gaps	**Using and applying mathematics:** describe simple patterns and relationships using numbers
	43	Bounce numbers	**Calculating:** use practical and informal written methods to support the subtraction of a one-digit number from a one-digit or two-digit number
		Doubling up	**Knowing and using number facts:** recall the doubles of all numbers to at least 10
Number words	46	Double partners	**Knowing and using number facts:** recall the doubles of all numbers to at least 10
		Whisper numbers	**Counting and understanding number:** read numerals from 0 to 20
	47	Can you read me?	**Calculating:** use the vocabulary related to addition and symbols to describe and record addition number sentences
		High fives!	**Counting and understanding number:** read and write numerals from 0 to 20

ABACUS

The abacus tool follows the conventions of a standard decimal abacus. Beads can be dragged onto or off the abacus to make different totals. Clicking the 'random' button will generate either a random number of beads on the abacus, or a random target number. The user can choose to show an abacus with either two or three spikes.

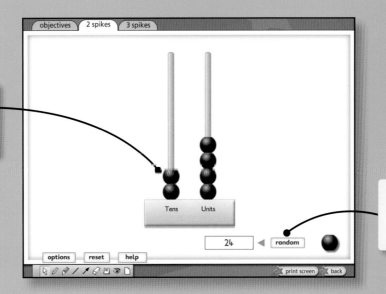

Drag and drop beads
Beads can be dragged onto or away from the abacus spikes.

Random button
Click to create a random target number or a random number of beads.

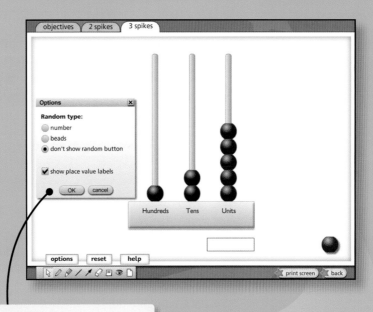

Tool functions

- Drag and drop beads onto the abacus
- 'Random' button creates random target numbers or number of beads
- Option to display/hide place value labels

Options
- Create a random number of beads on the abacus or a random target number in the box.
- Display/hide place value labels.

Activity type

Whole class

Learning objective

Knowing and using number facts: count on or back in ones and tens

Grab the beads

What to do

- Open the '2 spikes' screen. In the options menu, select random type 'number'.
- Click the 'random' button to generate a random number on the screen. Ask the children to read the number. Place the correct number of beads on the abacus by dragging them from the bottom right corner of the screen and dropping them onto the relevant spikes.
- Ask the children to discuss what you would have to do if you wanted to increase the number by 1.
- Invite one child to demonstrate and ask another child to predict what they think the new number will be.
- Now increase the number by 10, using the keypad. Ask: *Where would you place a bead to represent this new number?*
- Repeat with other numbers, increasing or decreasing by 1 or 10.

Key questions

- *What is different about the beads on the columns?*
- *How many beads can you fit onto one column? What happens if you add one more?*

Assessment for learning

Are the children able to count forward in ones and tens?

Activity type

Starter

Learning objective

Calculating: understand subtraction as 'take away'

Going down

What to do

- Open the '2 spikes' screen. In the options menu, select random type 'beads'.
- Click the 'random' button to generate a random arrangement of beads. Ask the children what the number is and make a note of it on the board.
- Explain to the children that you are going to change the number by taking one bead away. Ask them to close their eyes and then take away a bead while their eyes are shut.
- Encourage the children to agree in pairs what the new number is, and to work out which bead has been taken away.
- Repeat the activity. As the children improve, take two beads away.

Key questions

- *How many beads are in the units column?*
- *If I take away one bead, how many beads are left?*

Assessment for learning

Do the children understand subtraction as 'taking away'?

Activity type

Group

Learning objective

Calculating: use practical and informal written methods to support the addition of a one-digit number or a multiple of 10 to a one-digit or two-digit number

Big numbers

What to do

- Open the '2 spikes' screen. Explain to the children that they are going to be writing addition number sentences. Make sure they know what an addition sign looks like and write it on the board if necessary. Ask them how they would write down 'three add twenty-four'.
- Choose a one-digit number and write it on the board. Ask the children how many beads that number represents.
- Click the 'random' button to create a two-digit number. Explain that the one-digit number and the two-digit abacus number are two parts of a number sentence; demonstrate how to set it out. Ask: *What can we do with the abacus to help us complete the number sentence?*
- Repeat with new numbers.
- When the children are confident, change the one-digit number to a multiple of 10.

Key questions

- *Have you checked with your partner that you have written your number sentences correctly?*
- *What happens when you have more than nine beads on the abacus?*

Assessment for learning

Do the children have a strategy when using the abacus to add?

Activity type

Paired assessment

Learning objective

Knowing and using number facts: count on or back in tens

New beads from old

What to do

- Open the '3 spikes' screen. In the options menu, select random type 'beads'.
- Explain to the children that they are going to change an abacus number by a multiple of 10 to create 30 more or 30 less.
- Click the 'random' button to generate a two-digit number of beads (or simply make a number between 31 and 69 using the abacus beads). Ask the children to create the two new numbers by adding or taking away three beads.
- Hand out copies of photocopiable page 12 for the children to keep a record of both new numbers, as well as the bead patterns on the abacus.
- Once they have done this, repeat the exercise with a new two-digit number. Tell the children to complete the lower half of the photocopiable sheet to make a note of the new numbers and patterns.

Key questions

- *What happens when you have more than nine beads on the abacus? 99 beads?*
- *What happens when you add ten beads to the abacus? 20 beads?*

Assessment for learning

Do the children have useful strategies for counting in tens?

Name _____   Date _____

New beads from old

◾ Write down the numbers you make when you add/take away
30 beads from the abacus. Draw the beads on the abacus.

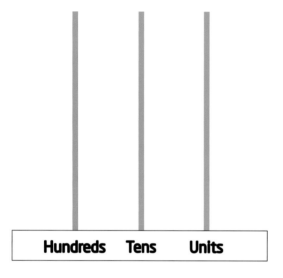

| Hundreds | Tens | Units |

Original number: _____

30 more: _____

| Hundreds | Tens | Units |

Original number: _____

30 less: _____

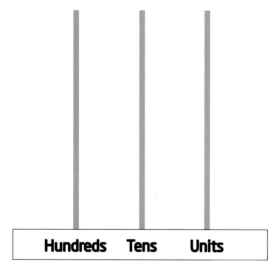

| Hundreds | Tens | Units |

Original number: _____

30 more: _____

| Hundreds | Tens | Units |

Original number: _____

30 less: _____

Star Maths Tools ★ Year 1
PHOTOCOPIABLE

CLOCKS

This is a flexible tool that allows you to display either one or two analogue or digital clocks per screen. The options menu allows the times on any clock to be randomised to the nearest minute, 5 minutes, 15 minutes, half-hour or hour.

Show numbers/minutes
Show or hide numbers or minute markers.

Link hands
Select to drag both hands in synchronicity.

Reset
Click to reset clock times.

Time set
Adjust hours and minutes separately.

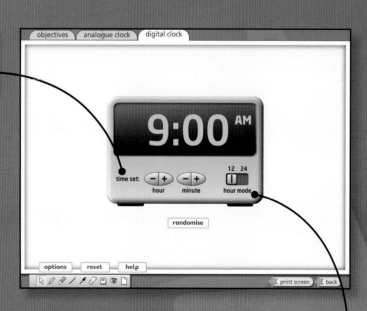

Tool functions

- 'Randomise' creates a random time on each clock
- Numbers or minute markers may be hidden
- Analogue clock hands may be moved to any time
- Digital time may be displayed in 12- or 24-hour clock mode

Hour mode
Display 12- or 24-hour times.

Activity type

Whole class

Learning objective

Measuring: read the time to the hour and half-hour

Daily routine

What to do

- Select the analogue clock tab at the top of the screen.
- Ask the children to discuss what time they usually get up. Explain that in today's lesson they are going to show what their daily routine looks like on a series of clock faces.
- Set the clock to 7.00. What do the children think happens then? Repeat with other times to the hour and half-hour.
- The children should use the empty clock faces on photocopiable page 16 to plot key parts of their daily routine. When they have done this, ask them when their daily routines change. For example, are they different at weekends or on holidays? Why do they change?

Key questions

- *What is part of your daily routine? What time do you get up? When do you have breakfast? What time does school start? What else do you do everyday? Can you show me these times on the clock?*
- *Do you have clocks at home? Where are they? Why are they in those places?*

Assessment for learning

Are the children able to read the time to the hour and half-hour and relate it to their daily routine?

Activity type

Starter

Learning objective

Measuring: read the time to the hour

Ding dong!

What to do

- Explain to the children that, unfortunately, the bells of Big Ben (or another more local bell tower) are not working and that they must help by calling out the bells.
- Open the analogue clock screen. As a class, read/chant the numbers round the face of the clock.
- Tell the children to pretend they are Big Ben. Ask: *How would you sound 1 o'clock?* (Call out 'dong!') *What about 2 o'clock?* (Call out 'dong! dong!')
- When the children have got the idea, click 'randomise' to set a new random time on the clock (use the options menu to change the randomisation to the nearest hour). Ask the children what time the clock now shows. How many 'dongs' are needed? Sound out the dongs.
- Repeat with new times, using the randomise option.

Key questions

- *How many rings will there be for 4 o'clock?*
- *Can you show me 6 o'clock on this clock?*

Assessment for learning

Are the children able to read the time to the hour?

Time challenge

Learning objective

Counting and understanding number: say the number that is 1 more or less than any given number

What to do

- In the options menu, select two analogue clock faces with linked hands. Randomly set the time (use the default setting, which is set to randomise to the nearest half-hour).
- Explain to the children that they are going to work as two teams: Team A will set the clock; Team B must set the second clock so that it is either an hour ahead of or an hour behind Team A's.
- Examine each clock. Ask the children what time each clock shows.
- Swap sides and repeat the activity.

Key questions

- *What do you need to look at to work out the change of time?*
- *What happens to the minute hand?*

Assessment for learning

Are the children able to read the time one hour ahead of or behind the target time?

Tell the time

Activity type

Paired assessment

Learning objective

Measuring: read the time to the hour and half-hour

What to do

- Open the analogue clock screen. Use the default setting in the options menu, which is set to randomise to the nearest half-hour.
- Explain to the children that you are going to see whether they are able to read the time. All times will be either on the hour or half past the hour.
- Click the 'randomise' button to display a range of times on the clock face. Each time, check that the children can state whether the time is half past or on the hour.
- Once the children are confident at this, assess whether they can read the exact time (for example: nine o'clock, half past eight).
- Repeat with new random clock faces.
- Ask the children to come to the board to set different times on the clock.

Key questions

- *How do you know whether it is half past twelve or six o'clock?*
- *What do the different hands do?*

Assessment for learning

Are the children able to read times on the hour and half past the hour?

Name _____ Date _____

Daily routine

◾ Write down some of the things you do everyday. Draw in the hands on the clocks to show the times.

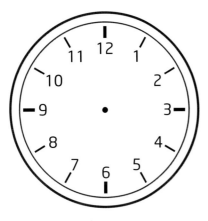

_____

_____

_____

_____

_____

_____

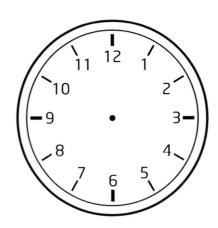

_____

_____

CONNECT BRICKS

This tool moves the familiar classroom resource to the interactive whiteboard. With a limitless supply of bricks and five colours to choose from, the user can create a wide range of number and colour patterns. In combination with the teacher's tools, number patterns and number sentences can be demonstrated to children of a wide range of abilities.

Drag and drop
Drag bricks from the palette to the working area.

Move
Double-click on a group of bricks to move them as a whole group.

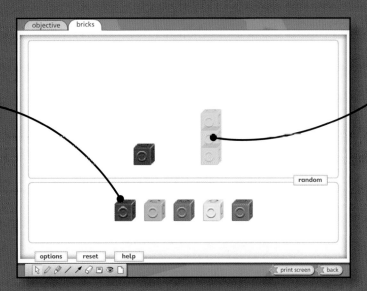

Random button
Click to generate a random number of bricks within pre-set limits.

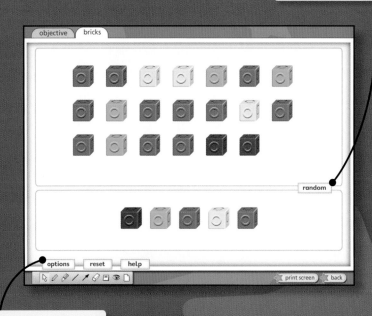

Tool functions

- Drag and drop bricks onto the working area
- 'Random' button creates a random number of bricks within pre-set parameters
- Option to define maximum and minimum number of bricks

Options
Choose whether bricks should click together automatically.

Activity type

Whole class

Learning objective

Calculating: solve practical problems that involve sharing into equal groups

Sharing strawberries

What to do

- Ask the class what they would do if they had a bag of strawberries and they wanted each of their friends to have the same number.
- Explain that you have a tool to help with this sharing problem.
- Open the Connect bricks tool. Click the 'random' button to display a random number of bricks on the screen.
- Explain that you are going to share the bricks shown on the screen among three children. Using either the pen or a sticky note from the teacher's toolbox, write three names at the top of the board. Using one of the methods that the children suggested for sharing strawberries, drag equal numbers of bricks and drop them under the names.
- Repeat with another random number set of bricks.

Key questions

- *Do the colours of the bricks matter when sharing?*
- *How many bricks did you share altogether? What do we do if we have spare bricks?*

Assessment for learning

Are the children able to sort the bricks into equal groups?

Activity type

Starter

Learning objective

Calculating: count reliably, recognising that when rearranged the number of objects stays the same

Mix the bricks

What to do

- Invite a child to come to the board to 'grab' an assortment of bricks from the lower tray and drop them onto the working area above.
- As a class, count the total number of bricks on the screen. Use a sticky note from the teacher's toolbox to make a note of this number.
- Explain that you are now going to mix the bricks, before moving them around on the screen.
- Move the bricks, then ask the children if they think the total number of bricks has changed. Count them again. (There will be the same number.) Tell the children that you are sure that if you mix them enough times, the number will change. Mix them again. By now the children should be able to state with confidence that the number will, in fact, remain the same.

Key questions

- *When we move the bricks around, does the total number of bricks change?*
- *What would we need to do to make the total number change?*

Assessment for learning

Do the children understand that the amount does not change even when the bricks are mixed up?

Picture a number

Activity type

Group

Learning objective

Calculating: use the vocabulary related to addition and symbols to describe and record addition number sentences

What to do

- Explain to the children that they are going to make numbers with their number bricks and on the board.
- Use the pen from the teacher's toolbox to write a one-digit number sentence (for example, 5 + 3 = ___) at the top of the screen. Ask the children how they could use the bricks to show the numbers in your sentence.
- Drag bricks from the brick tray and drop them beneath the numbers you have written on the screen. Use the bricks to help the children complete the addition sentence. Read out the sentence, emphasising the symbols.
- Now ask the children to create their own one-digit number sentences and show them with bricks. Tell them to record their answers on photocopiable page 20.

Key questions

- *How can you use the bricks to work out the final answer?*
- *Does it matter what colour bricks you use?*

Assessment for learning

Are the children able to read both numbers and addition symbols in a number sentence?

Grab three

Activity type

Paired assessment

Learning objective

Using and applying mathematics: describe simple patterns and relationships involving numbers

What to do

- Using a sticky note from the teacher's toolbox, write a target number on the screen (for example, 3).
- Explain to the children that they are to grab three of each colour brick. In their pairs, they are to organise them on the screen in whichever way they choose.
- Once they have done this, ask the children why they organised the bricks in the way they did. What discussion did they have? Ask: *Could you organise the bricks in another way? If you had fewer colours, would you change the pattern? How could your pattern help with your number work?* (For example, if the bricks were arranged in groups of three, the pattern could help with adding on.)

Key questions

- *Why have you organised your bricks like this?*
- *How can you best organise the bricks to help you with counting in groups?*

Assessment for learning

Do the children understand that patterns can be made from numbers?

Name _____   Date _____

Picture a number

■ Write digits in the boxes to make a number sentence.

■ Draw bricks to show the number sentence in the space below.

 +  =

 +  =

 + 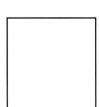 =

Star Maths Tools ★ Year 1
PHOTOCOPIABLE

COUNTING BEARS

This tool allows the user to demonstrate sorting and counting activities with familiar objects. Assorted images (in different sizes and/or colours) enable the user to create a variety of stimulating and fun lessons for young children.

Drag and drop

Drag images from the palette and drop them onto the working area.

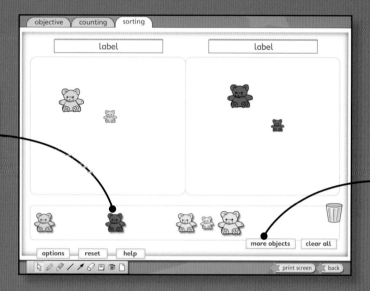

More objects

Click to display a further range of objects to use.

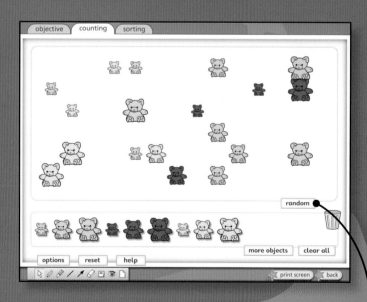

Tool functions

- Drag and drop images to and from the palette
- Choose from a range of different images
- 'Random' button generates a random number of items within pre-defined limits

Random button

Click to generate a random number of items for counting or sorting.

Activity type

Activity type

Starter

Learning objective

Calculating: solve practical problems that involve sharing into equal groups

Teddy bears' picnic

What to do

- Select three bears from the image palette and drop them onto the working area. Next, click on 'more objects', go to the images of fruit and vegetables, and select nine apples (or similar).
- Explain to the children that the three teddy bears are going on a picnic - they need the children's help to share their food. Invite the children to discuss in pairs how they would share the food (note whether any children actually count the apples that are displayed on the screen). Encourage them to explain their strategies.
- Now share out the nine apples by dragging and dropping equal numbers next to each bear. Ask: *How many apples does each bear have?*
- Finally, ask the children to imagine that each bear has one more apple. How many apples would there be on the screen?
- For further practice, ask the children to complete photocopiable page 24.

Key questions

- *Have you ever been on a picnic? How did you share your food?*
- *What is the best way of sharing out the apples so that each bear has the same number?*

Assessment for learning

What strategies do the children use to share the fruit into equal groups?

Activity type

Whole class

Learning objective

Calculating: understand subtraction as 'take away'

Healthy eating

What to do

- Click on 'more objects' and select the images of fruit and vegetables. Ask: *Can you see any of your favourite fruits or vegetables here?*
- Invite each child to choose one fruit or vegetable from the image palette and to drag it onto the working area.
- As a class, count the total number of fruits and vegetables. Use either the pen or the sticky note from the teacher's toolbox to record the result on the screen.
- Next, ask the children to group the fruits and vegetables in any way they choose.
- Use the children's groupings to create some subtraction sentences. For example, subtract carrots from the whole number, then ask the children what is left. Write the subtraction sentence on the screen (for example, 28 - 6 = 22) and invite the class to chant the sentence.

Key questions

- *How can we find out how many fruits and vegetables are left on the screen?*
- *What would happen if we put the carrots back and took away another vegetable group?*

Assessment for learning

Can the children sort the items into useful groups that can be taken away from the total number of objects?

Activity type

Group

Learning objective

Counting and understanding number: count reliably at least 20 objects, recognising that when rearranged the number of objects stays the same

What a mix-up!

What to do

- Invite the children to choose one of the images available (either one of the bears, or an image from the 'more objects' array).
- Drag between 12 and 20 images onto the screen (or click the 'random' button, which is pre-set to generate up to 20 items). Ask the group to count the objects.
- Explain that you are now going to move the objects around, and ask whether this will make a difference to the total.
- Move the objects around, then check whether the total has changed.
- Clear the screen, then invite a member of the group to come to the board and drag and drop more than ten objects. Count the objects with the group, then invite the lead child to move them around. Has the total number of objects changed?
- As a follow-up activity, open the sorting screen and arrange two sets of objects into groups. Count each group to identify which group has more or less.

Key questions

- *How do you know that the number does not change?*
- *What would we need to do to change the total?*

Assessment for learning

Can the children recognise that the total number does not change even when the individual items are rearranged?

Activity type

Review

Learning objective

Counting and understanding number: estimate a number of objects that can be checked by counting

How many?

What to do

- Click the 'random' button to display a random number of bears on the screen (by default, the maximum number of bears that can be generated in this way is set at 20, but this number can be changed in the options menu if necessary).
- Explain that, because you know your numbers to 20, you don't have to count the bears. You can estimate how many are on the screen by looking. Make an estimate, then count to see how close you were.
- Ask the children if they would like to have a go at estimating the number. Click the 'random' button again to create a new set of bears. Invite the children to discuss in pairs what they think the total is before counting.
- When the children have gained some confidence in estimating, ask them to record their predictions on their individual whiteboards (or sheets of paper).
- Encourage the children to share their estimates with the rest of the class before they count the bears on the screen.

Key questions

- *What strategies can you use to estimate the number on the screen?*
- *Do you think you will get better the more times you try this?*

Assessment for learning

Are the children able to accurately estimate how many objects are on the screen?

Name _____ Date _____

Teddy bears' picnic

◪ Share the fruit equally between the bears.

1. Each has _____ apple.

2. Each has _____ bananas.

 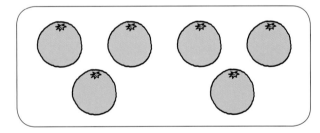

3. Each has _____ oranges.

4. Each has _____ apples.

Star Maths Tools ★ Year 1
PHOTOCOPIABLE

MONEY

This tool allows the user to demonstrate money problems using realistic-looking coins. A limitless number of coins can be dragged onto the screen. Using the teacher's tools, a wide range of money-based activities can be set.

Drag and drop
Drag coins onto or off the working area.

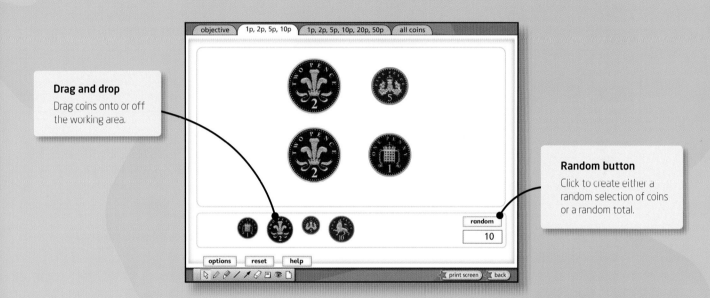

Random button
Click to create either a random selection of coins or a random total.

Options
Change the randomisation (coins or total).

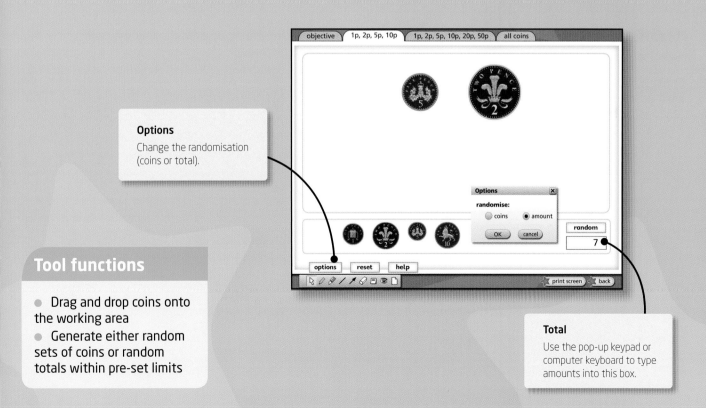

Total
Use the pop-up keypad or computer keyboard to type amounts into this box.

Tool functions

- Drag and drop coins onto the working area
- Generate either random sets of coins or random totals within pre-set limits

Activity type

Whole class

Learning objective

Using and applying mathematics: solve problems involving counting money, for example to 'pay' and 'give change'

Penny chews

What to do

- Open the '1p, 2p, 5p, 10p' screen. In the options menu, set randomise to 'amount'.
- Tell the class that you have just been shopping and that you have bought some penny sweets. Reveal how much they cost altogether (click the 'random' button to reveal a random penny price).
- Recap the different types of coins with the class, then ask the children what coins they think would be needed to pay for the sweets. They should use only the coins shown on the screen (they can have multiples), and record their answers on their individual whiteboards or sheets of paper. Explain that, unfortunately, they cannot get change, but the shopkeeper would like the payment to be as close as possible to the total amount (either more or less).
- Discuss some of the children's payments and illustrate them by dragging and dropping coins onto the working area. How close have the children got to the total?

Key questions

- *If you paid with 20p, how would you work out how much change you would need?*
- *Is it easier to find the exact amount of money or to give a larger amount and expect change? Why?*

Assessment for learning

Can the children identify an amount that is equal to, or more than, the cost of the sweets?

Activity type

Starter

Learning objective

Using and applying mathematics: solve problems involving money

A big problem!

What to do

- Open the '1p, 2p, 5p, 10p, 20p and 50p' screen. By default, only the coin denominations of 50p or less will be displayed.
- Explain to the children that you have a problem – you can't remember what coins add up to 10p.
- Ask the children to discuss, in small groups, what coins they could use to make 10p. Share each group's conclusions with the rest of the class by dragging and dropping different combinations of coins onto the working area.
- Thank the class but say that you now have a bigger problem – you can't remember what coins add up to 20p.
- Repeat the process with different denominations of coins.

Key questions

- *How can you find the total using the fewest/most coins?*
- *What did you do to add up to the figure? Did you use different types of coin?*

Assessment for learning

Can the children add different denominations to find a target number?

Activity type

Group

Learning objective

Using and applying mathematics: solve problems involving adding money

Crazy coins

What to do

- Open the '1p, 2p, 5p, 10p, 20p and 50p' screen. In the options menu, set randomise to 'coins'.
- Explain that you have some crazy coins that are just waiting to fly onto the money pad. When they fly up, the class has to add all the coins that you state – for example, you might ask them to add all the brown coins, or all the 5-pence pieces.
- Click the 'random' button and ask the children to count the pennies (1-pence and 2-pence pieces). Remove these coins by dragging them from the working area and dropping them back into the image palette at the foot of the screen.
- Next, ask the children to count the 5-pence pieces, then remove them.
- Click the 'random' button again and invite a child to choose what should be counted.
- Ask the children to copy the set of random coins onto photocopiable page 28, then challenge a partner to count their chosen coins.

Key questions

- *When counting 5-pence pieces, what tools can we use to count with? (For example, our fingers.)*
- *Why are some coins larger than others?*

Assessment for learning

Can the children count sets of coins?

Activity type

Paired assessment

Learning objective

Counting and understanding number: compare and order numbers

Money towers

What to do

- Open the 'all coins' screen. In the options menu, set randomise to 'coins'.
- Explain to the children that they are going to create money towers from the random selection of coins displayed on the screen.
- Click the 'random' button to produce a set of coins. Drag the coins across the screen, arranging them in towers made of the same value coins, with the lowest value tower on the left and the highest value tower on the right. Talk about the different values, and ask the key questions below.
- Repeat the activity by clicking the 'random' button again, to produce a new set of coins for the children to order.

Key questions

- *What is the total of the tower made from the lowest value coin?*
- *How many 2-pence pieces do you have and what is their total?*

Assessment for learning

Can the children order random coins?

Name _____   Date _____

Crazy coins

■ Using the template below, fill in your crazy coins and challenge your partner to find the totals.

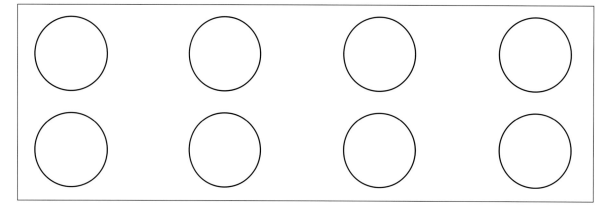

◻ How many 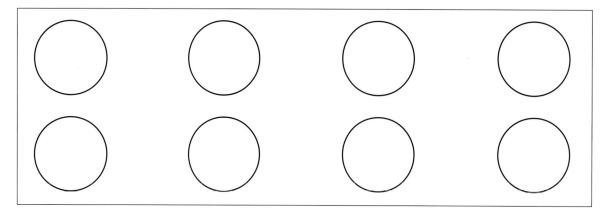 coins? _____

◻ How many coins? _____

◻ What is the total value of all the coins? _____

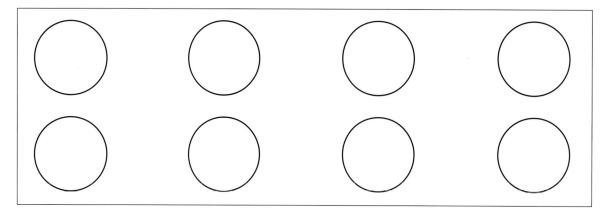

◻ How many coins? _____

◻ How many coins? _____

◻ What is the total value of all the coins? _____

Star Maths Tools ★ Year 1
PHOTOCOPIABLE

NUMBER FAN

This tool provides a giant version of the classroom classic resource. The fan has a range of options that have the same simple drag-and-drop functionality. A range of different fan sets is available, including numbers, 2D and 3D shapes, money, days and months.

Display
Display and re-order up to three sections of the fan at one time.

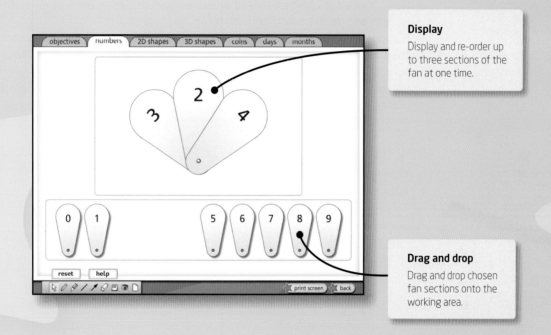

Drag and drop
Drag and drop chosen fan sections onto the working area.

Fan selection
Click on tab to select type of fan set.

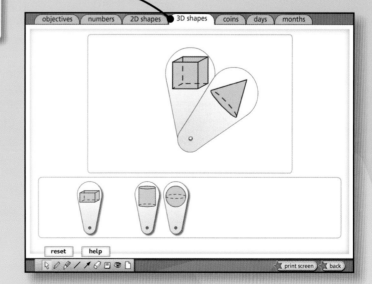

Tool functions

- Drag and drop fan sections onto the working area
- Wide range of fan sets

What shape is it?

Activity type

Whole class

Learning objective

Understanding shape: visualise and name common 2D shapes and describe their features

What to do

- Open the '2D shapes' screen.
- Drag a square from the palette and drop it onto the working area. Ask: *How would you describe this shape? What would be good describing words?* Use a sticky note from the teacher's toolbox to make a note of the children's responses so that they can be referred to later.
- Next, invite the children to find a partner and sit facing each other, with one partner facing the board and the other facing away.
- Explain that the partner facing the board is going to describe a selected shape; their partner is to try to guess what shape they are describing and move the shape onto the working area when it has been identified.
- Repeat the activity with a range of different shapes, and with partners swapping places. You could tell the children that they must ask questions that can be answered only with 'yes' or 'no' responses.

Key questions

- *How would you describe this shape?*
- *Which shapes did you find hardest to describe? Why?*

Assessment for learning

Are the children able to visualise 2D shapes and describe them accurately?

Forwards and backwards

Activity type

Starter

Learning objective

Knowing and using number facts: count on or back in ones

What to do

- For this activity, each child will need their own number fan.
- Open the 'numbers' screen and use the fan sections to create a two-digit number (for example, 23). Ask the children to show the same number on their fans. Explain that you are going to count forwards or backwards in ones as a warm-up exercise.
- Ask: *What would be one more than 23?* Invite the children to show the answer on their fans.
- Explain that if you say 'forwards' they must add 1; if you say 'backwards' they must take 1 away. Randomly chant 'forwards'/'backwards', giving the children enough time to change the numbers on their fans.
- Invite different children to take on the role of the chanter and to move new numbers onto the board.

Key questions

- *What is one more than _____? What is one less than _____?*
- *What do we have to do when we add 1 to a number ending in 9?*

Assessment for learning

Can the children confidently count on and back in ones?

Activity type

Activity type

Group

Learning objective

Knowing and using number facts: derive and recall addition facts for totals to at least 5

Partner numbers

What to do

- Open the 'numbers' screen. Explain to the children that they are going to find a missing number from a pair of numbers.
- Ask a child for a target number between 2 and 10. Make a note of this target number on the board, using a sticky note from the teacher's toolbox.
- Invite the children to find pairs of numbers that total the target. Discuss what numbers they cannot use (for example, if the target is 8, they cannot use 8 or 9). Ask them to show two numbers that make the target number on their number fans.
- Using the on-screen number fan, show a number less than the target number. Ask the children to find the partner number, to make their target.
- Repeat the activity with a second number less than the target number. Let the children use photocopiable page 32 to record the number pairs.

Key questions

- *Can we write down these numbers in a sentence to help us remember them? What would the number sentence look like?* (Use a sticky note to record the number sentence on the board in digits and symbols.)
- *What would be the largest number we could use that would have a partner number to make 5... 10? (and so on)*

Assessment for learning

Can the children find pairs of numbers that make totals up to 10?

Activity type

Paired assessment

Learning objective

Measuring: order months

Mixed months

What to do

- Open the 'months' screen.
- Organise the children to work in pairs: one partner has a small individual whiteboard and the other uses the number fan tool on the screen.
- Explain that the child using the on-screen tool should display three consecutive months, but jumbled up; they must challenge their partner to write the months in the correct order on their whiteboard.
- When the child with the whiteboard has decided on their answer, they should turn away while the child with the tool re-organises the sections of the fan into what they think is the correct order.
- Encourage the partners to compare their answers before swapping places to repeat the activity.

Key questions

- *How do you know your months are in the correct order?*
- *Which month comes after _____? Which month comes before _____?*

Assessment for learning

Are the children able to order the months of the year correctly?

Name _____   Date _____

Partner numbers

 Make these target numbers.

Target numbers	Partner numbers

1. Make 5

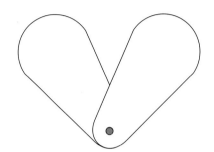

2. Make 8

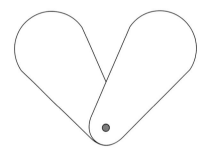

3. Make 6

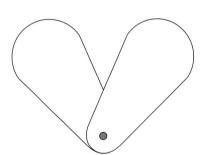

4. Make 10

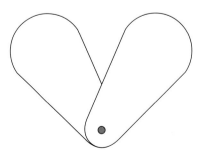

NUMBER SENTENCES

This tool allows the user to create mathematical sentences and problems on the screen. Parts can be added to, or removed from, the sentence at any point. Shape cards can be used to represent missing numbers.

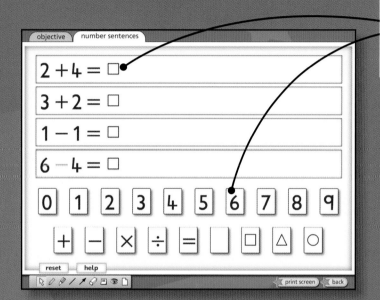

Drag and drop

Drag and drop number cards and symbols to create number sentences.

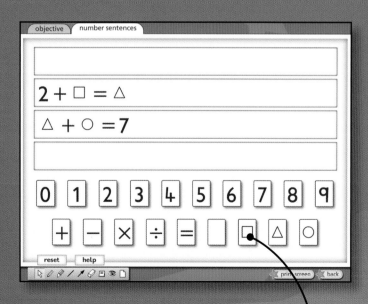

Shape cards

Use shape cards to create problems involving missing numbers.

Tool functions

- Drag and drop numbers or numbers and signs
- Use blank cards to create spaces between numbers and signs in sentences
- Drag cards out of the number sentence to edit or change it

Activity type

Starter

Learning objective

Counting and understanding number: say the number that is 1 more or less than any given number

One more/one less

What to do

- Drag the cards '+ 1' onto the top line, and '– 1' onto the second line.
- Explain to the children that today they are going to add 1 to and take 1 from any number. Ask a volunteer to suggest a number (for example, 23). Drag the number cards for 23 to the beginning of each row.
- Now ask the children to discuss, in pairs, what they think the answer is to each question. Take suggestions from the class, then drag the '=' sign and the relevant number cards to display the two answers on the relevant lines.
- Repeat the activity on the next two blank lines, using a different starting number.

Key questions

- *What happens if we add or take away 1?*
- *What is one more than ____? What is one less than ____?*

Assessment for learning

Can the children add or take away 1 from one-digit or two-digit numbers?

Activity type

Whole class

Learning objective

Knowing and using number facts: count on or back in ones, twos, fives and tens

Finger on/finger off

What to do

- Drag '+ 1', '+ 2', '+ 5' and '+ 10' to the four empty lines.
- Ask the children for a two-digit number (for example, 17). Explain that they are going to add each of the numbers on the screen to their chosen number. Drag the number cards for 17 to the beginning of each row.
- Explain that when adding or taking away it is always useful to use something to count with. Ask: *Can anybody in the class suggest something we can use to count with?* (Wave your fingers around as a clue!)
- Encourage the children to use their fingers as counting tools to complete the number sentences. Drag the relevant cards to display the answers on the four lines.
- Now remove the results and replace the addition sign with the subtraction sign. Ask the children to subtract each of the numbers on the screen from 17 to complete the new number sentences.
- Hand out copies of photocopiable page 36 for the children to create their own addition and subtraction sentences.

Key questions

- *What is the same in each sentence and what is different?*
- *What is the difference between the addition and subtraction sentences and what is similar?*

Assessment for learning

Are the children able to count on or back successfully?

Activity type

Group

Learning objective

Calculating: use the vocabulary related to addition and subtraction and symbols to describe and record addition and subtraction number sentences

Mystery sentence

What to do

- Ask the children to discuss what types of cards are available. Draw attention to the shape cards. Ask: *What could these cards be used for?*
- Explain that you are going to create some mystery sentences using the numbers, symbols and shapes. Model a mystery sentence by creating an addition sentence (for example, 4 + 9 = 13). Replace one of the three numbers with a shape card. Ask the children whether hiding the number has changed the number sentence.
- Now create a mystery sentence with a shape card already in place. Encourage the children to discuss what number might be hidden by the shape, assuming the sentence is true.
- Split the children into two smaller groups: ask each group to create mystery sentences for the other group to solve, using a shape card in place of one of the numbers in each sentence. Tell them that they must know the answers to their mystery sentences before asking the other group to solve them!

Key questions

- *If the first or the second number is hidden by a shape, how can you find its value?*
- *If two numbers were hidden by shapes, could you find their values? How?*

Assessment for learning

Do the children understand that the value of the number sentence stays the same despite one element being hidden?

Activity type

Paired assessment

Learning objective

Knowing and using number facts: recall the doubles of all numbers to at least 10

Double up

What to do

- Explain to the children that they are going to create a pattern of number sentences to show doubling.
- Demonstrate by dragging and dropping the relevant number and sign cards to show 1 + 1 = 2 in the top row. Ask: *What might be the next number sentence in the pattern?* The children may suggest doubling the result only (in this case 2), but guide them instead towards doubling each component of the number sentence: 2 + 2 = 4.
- Explain that four 'doubling' sentences can be created on the screen. Ask: *What do you think the last sentence would be?* Start the children on the task.
- When the first four number sentences have been completed, you can print the screen and reset it, before continuing with '5 + 5'.

Key questions

- *What do I mean when I say I want to double something?*
- *What do you notice about all the numbers once they are ordered?*

Assessment for learning

Are the children able to see any patterns in the numbers?

Name _____ Date _____

It all adds up!

◾ Think of a two-digit number and write it in these boxes.

◾ Write your two-digit number at the beginning of each of the rows below.

◾ Find the answer to each of the number sentences.

	+	1	=

	+	2	=

	+	5	=

	+	10	=

	−	1	=

	−	2	=

	−	5	=

	−	10	=

NUMBER SQUARE

This tool is a flexible version of familiar number squares, and includes a 100-square, addition square and multiplication square. The user is able to adjust the shape of the square and the number range to create the specific resource they require. The grids can also be printed out for individual or class use.

Teacher tools

Use sticky notes to annotate.

Grid tools

Change background colour, hide, highlight, edit and drag squares off the grid.

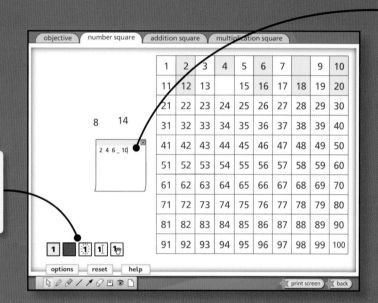

Numbers

- Drag numbers from the grid.
- Input numbers into the grid.

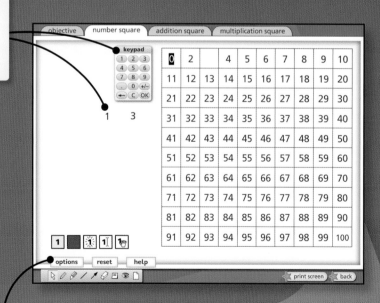

Tool functions

- Columns and rows adjustable
- Start number adjustable
- Highlight, hide and reveal buttons
- Step number adjustable
- Hide/reveal individual numbers or whole rows
- Print grid
- Drag numbers off the square
- Input numbers into the square

Options

Create bespoke squares quickly using the pre-set numbers.

Activity type

Whole class

Learning objective

Knowing and using number facts: count on or back in ones, twos, fives and tens and use this knowledge to derive the multiples of 2, 5 and 10 to the tenth multiple

Match multiples

What to do

- Open the number square screen, which by default is set to display a 100-square. Explain to the children that they are going to count on in twos, starting at 2. Highlight the numbers 2, 4, 6, 8… in yellow as the children count.
- Now count in fives, starting at 5 (highlight in green).
- Finally, count in tens, starting at 10 (highlight in pink).
- Ask the children to discuss what has happened to some of the numbers, such as 10.
- Now open the multiplication square screen. In the options menu, select pre-set configuration to show the 2-, 5- and 10-times tables. Ask: *Are the numbers in these sequences the same as the numbers that were highlighted in the 100-square?*
- Ask the children what numbers from the 2-times tables are in both the 5- and 10-times tables. Highlight these numbers in yellow.

Key questions

- *Why do some of the numbers, such as 10, change colour? Are they yellow, green or pink, or could they be all three?*
- *Can anyone see any numbers that are in all three groups?*

Assessment for learning

Do the children understand that one number can be a multiple of more than one other number?

Activity type

Group

Learning objective

Calculating: relate addition to counting on

What's ahead and what's behind?

What to do

- Open the number square screen. Use the options menu to edit the 100-square so that it has only three rows and ten columns. By default it will start at 1 and go up in ones to 30. Use the blue 'hide' button to hide all the numbers.
- Now use the 'reveal' button to reveal three consecutive numbers from the middle row. Ask the children to discuss what they think the next number will be. Take answers from the class.
- Next, create a new 3 × 10 number grid, but this time change the step to '2' in the options menu. Again, hide all the numbers.
- Reveal three consecutive numbers from the middle row. Ask the children to discuss what is different. What do they need to do to find the next number?
- When the children have worked out that the numbers are going up in twos, reveal the previous number in the row. Ask: *Can you predict what the next number back will be?*
- Repeat the activity with different start numbers.

Key questions

- *How can you use the number patterns to work out the next number?*
- *If we are going up in ones, does it matter if the start number is different?*

Assessment for learning

Can the children predict number patterns and count on?

Activity type

Starter

Learning objective

Using and applying mathematics: describe simple patterns and relationships involving numbers

Colour squares

What to do

- Open the number square screen. Use the options menu to change the 100-square so that it has only three rows and ten columns. On this 1–30 grid, colour the first three squares red, then choose another colour with which to highlight the next three squares.
- Ask the children to discuss in pairs what your colour pattern rule might be. Meanwhile, choose more colours and continue your pattern.
- Invite a child to explain what the rule is. If they are correct, ask them to choose the next colour pattern rule.
- When they are confident, you can make the rule more complex. For example: *Follow two blue squares with three green squares, and repeat.*
- Working with partners, ask the children to continue devising colour rules using photocopiable page 40.

Key questions

- *How did you guess my rule? What other rules might there be?*
- *What could I have done to make my rule easier to guess?*

Assessment for learning

Can the children use colours to show simple number patterns and relationships?

Activity type

Group

Learning objective

Calculating: find a 'difference' by counting up

Joining numbers

What to do

- Open the number square screen. Use the options menu to edit the 100-square so that it has only two rows and ten columns.
- Highlight two non-adjacent numbers in the grid. Explain to the children that the largest number is the 'end number' and the lowest number is the 'start number'. Ask: *How can you find the difference between the two numbers?*
- Try out the children's suggestions on the board and agree on one idea. (Counting up.) Test it with new numbers to find their differences.
- Ask: *What would happen if we counted up in twos?*

Key questions

- *Do we always have to count up in ones to find a difference?*
- *Can we count up in twos?*
- *As we have lots of colours, can we use them to highlight the numbers we have counted?* (This is useful when counting in twos.)

Assessment for learning

Do the children have an efficient method to find a difference?

Name _____   Date _____

Colour squares

- Use the number squares below to create some number patterns.
- Now give your worksheet to a partner and ask them to work out your rules.

1	2	3	4	5	6	7	8	9	10
11	12	13	14	15	16	17	18	19	20
21	22	23	24	25	26	27	28	29	30

1	2	3	4	5	6	7	8	9	10
11	12	13	14	15	16	17	18	19	20
21	22	23	24	25	26	27	28	29	30

PHOTOCOPIABLE

NUMBER TRACK

The number track can be configured to start and end with any number, and can be displayed either vertically or horizontally. Sequences and patterns can be extended by scrolling forwards and backwards. Individual numbers can be highlighted or hidden and will remain coloured even if they have been scrolled off screen.

Highlighted numbers

Numbers remain coloured even if scrolled off the screen.

Hide/highlight

Six colours are available to hide or highlight numbers.

Edit

Use the edit button to change numbers in the track.

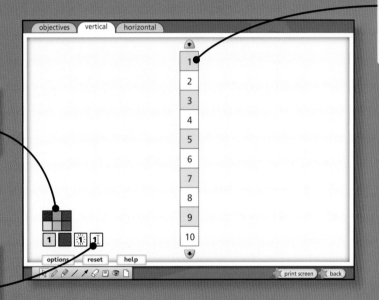

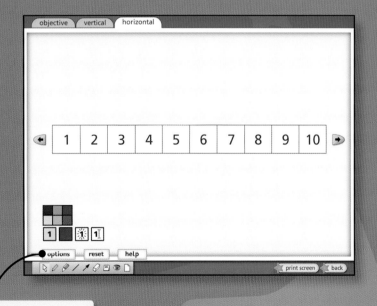

Tool functions

- Vertical or horizontal number track
- Edit numbers
- Highlight, hide and reveal numbers
- Options to change the range and the scrolling function

Options

Select whether to show the numbers in the track vertically or horizontally.

Activity type

Whole class

Learning objective

Knowing and using number facts: count on or back in ones, twos, fives and tens

Up and down numbers

What to do

- Open the vertical number track screen to reveal the default number track of 1-10.
- Explain to the children that they are going to count up and down the track.
- As a class, read out the numbers from bottom to top, then ask the children to suggest to each other what they think the next number will be. (11)
- In the options menu, set the track to start at 12 and end at 22. Set the scrollable range at 0 to 30. Read out the numbers as a class. This time, ask the children to discuss what number they think would appear before 12. Scroll back to check their answer.
- Now choose a step of 2, 5 or 10 in the options menu. Repeat the activity using the new track.

Key questions

- *How can you work out what the new step number is?*
- *What do you predict the next two answers will be?*

Assessment for learning

Can the children confidently count on and back in ones, twos, fives and tens?

Activity type

Starter

Learning objective

Using and applying mathematics: describe simple patterns and relationships using numbers

Fill the gaps

What to do

- Open the horizontal number track screen to reveal the default number track of 1-10. Select the blue 'hide' button and use it to hide five random squares.
- Ask the children to discuss in groups what they think are the missing numbers. Discuss their ideas, then reveal the missing numbers. Explain that the pattern is 'one more'. Check by scrolling on to the next number.
- Now set the track to start at 2 and end at 10, with a step of 2. Hide two numbers. Ask the children to discuss what numbers are missing. Explain that the pattern is '2 more'. Check by scrolling on to the next number.
- Use the options menu to set the track to start at 10 and end at 50, with a step of 10. Set the scrollable range at 0 to 100. Do not hide any numbers, but ask what number the children think will be next.

Key questions

- *How can the numbers in the track help you work out the missing numbers?*
- *What would help you to work out the missing numbers?*

Assessment for learning

Are the children using efficient strategies to help identify any patterns?

Activity type

Group

Learning objective

Calculating: use practical and informal written methods to support the subtraction of a one-digit number from a one-digit or two-digit number

Bounce numbers

What to do

- Open the horizontal number track screen. Use the options menu to set the track to start at 20 and end at 30; set the scrollable range at 0 to 30.
- Invite a child to choose a number from the track on the screen (for example, 27). Explain to the group that they are going to 'bounce back' from 27 until they are as close as possible to 1.
- Ask a child to suggest a one-digit bounce number (for example, 4). Starting at 27, repeatedly count back four places. Record your bounces by highlighting the relevant number squares or by removing them from the number track. When you get to 20, scroll backwards to 19 (and below). Keep recording the bounce steps backwards until you get as near to 1 as possible, without the number becoming negative.
- Hand out copies of photocopiable page 44 for the children to record their own 'bounce back' tracks. They should choose a start number between 10 and 20, using a one-digit bounce number from 1–5. How close can they get to 1? What happens if they use a different start number?

Key questions

- *What happens when we bounce back in steps of 2?*
- *How else can we show patterns of numbers?* (Use subtraction number sentences.)

Assessment for learning

Can the children accurately subtract a one-digit number from a two-digit number?

Activity type

Review

Learning objective

Knowing and using number facts: recall the doubles of all numbers to at least 10

Doubling up

What to do

- Open the vertical number track screen.
- Explain to the children that they are going to double all the numbers up to 10 within the next ten minutes by using two colours.
- Invite two children to choose two different colours from the colour palette. Explain that you are going to record the doubles on the board; use the pen from the teacher's toolbox to write the numbers 1 to 10 down the left-hand side.
- To find the double of 1, highlight the first block in the track one colour, and the next block the other colour. Ask the children to count the number of blocks on the number track to check that 1 + 1 = 2 . Record the double of 1 on the left-hand side of the board. Remove the highlights from the track.
- To find the double of 2, use the 'hide' tool to colour the first two blocks one colour, and the next two blocks the other colour. Repeat with the other numbers, encouraging the children to fill in the blocks and to check by counting the number of blocks on the track.

Key questions

- *Are there any doubles that you know already? For example, what is double 1 or 2?*
- *Is there a pattern to our doubles? What sort of numbers are they?* (They are even numbers.)

Assessment for learning

Do the children understand what doubling means, and how to double numbers to 10?

Name _____   Date _____

Bounce numbers

- Use these number lines to create your own 'bounce back' tracks.
- Write your bounce number.
- Choose a number between 10 and 20 and colour it in on the first number track. Bounce back until you get as close as possible to 1. Colour in each of the numbers you bounce on.
- Now complete the following three number lines, using a different bounce number each time.

Bounce number ☐

1	2	3	4	5	6	7	8	9	10	11	12	13	14	15	16	17	18	19	20

Bounce number ☐

1	2	3	4	5	6	7	8	9	10	11	12	13	14	15	16	17	18	19	20

Bounce number ☐

1	2	3	4	5	6	7	8	9	10	11	12	13	14	15	16	17	18	19	20

Bounce number ☐

1	2	3	4	5	6	7	8	9	10	11	12	13	14	15	16	17	18	19	20

NUMBER WORDS

Banks of words and numbers allow the user to create number sentences using one- and two-digit numbers. A random function creates a range of random numbers within any given parameters.

Random button
Click to generate a random number within pre-set parameters.

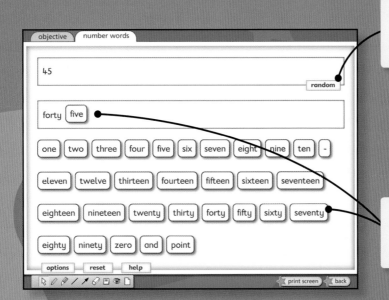

Number cards
Drag cards and drop them into empty box above.

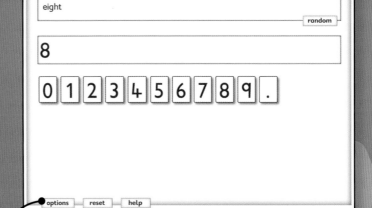

Tool functions

- Drag and drop numbers in words or figures
- Use 'random' button to generate random one- or two-digit numbers

Options
Select whether to use number cards or word cards.

Activity type

Whole class

Learning objective

Knowing and using number facts: recall the doubles of all numbers to at least 10

Double partners

What to do

- Select 'use word cards' in the options menu.
- Explain to the children that they are going to work with partners to find doubles of all numbers to at least 10. One child in each pair will write a number name less than 10 on their individual whiteboard (for example, 8) and their partner will read the number and then try to work out its double, using any strategy.
- Demonstrate by typing a number (less than 10) into the top box on the screen. Ask the children if they can find its double partner in the array of word cards displayed at the foot of the screen. Invite a volunteer to come to the board to drag and drop the word into the lower blank box on the screen.

Key questions

- *What is a double?*
- *Which row do you need to look in to find the double of the displayed number?*

Assessment for learning

Are the children able to recall the doubles of all numbers up to 10?

Activity type

Starter

Learning objective

Counting and understanding number: read numerals from 0 to 20

Whisper numbers

What to do

- 'Whisper numbers' is a call-out game for the whole class. By asking the children to whisper the numbers they see on the board, you should be able to assess how many children can read the number.
- In the options menu, select 'use digit cards'. To show a number between 0 and 20, select the relevant number cards and drag and drop them into the lower empty box on the screen.
- Give the children a few seconds to read the number you have displayed, then ask them to whisper its name. Confirm their answer by typing the name of the number into the top blank box.
- Repeat the activity, gradually introducing more complex numbers.

Key questions

- *How did you read the numbers? What helped you?*
- *Are there any similarities between the 'teen' numbers and the ones?*

Assessment for learning

Are the children able to read all numbers up to 20?

Can you read me?

What to do

- This activity introduces children to the concept of number sentences by writing them in words.
- In the options menu, select 'use word cards'. Using the pen from the teacher's toolbox, circle the cards showing the number words 'one', 'two', 'three', 'four' and 'five'. Explain that these are the numbers that the children will be writing.
- Use a sticky note from the teacher's toolbox to write a number sentence using the numbers 1 to 5 in figures (for example, 3 + 2 = 5). Ask the children to read the number sentence and then to sound out each individual number word, finding them in the bank of word cards as they read.
- Ask the children to record some of their own addition number sentences in both figures and words on photocopiable page 48.

Key questions

- *What do you know have five things?* (Help the children realise that the five digits on a hand can be used for counting numbers.)
- *Does the sentence look different when written? Why?*

Assessment for learning

Are the children able to create and read simple addition number sentences?

High fives!

What to do

- Explain to the children that they are going to be 'super spies' and look for word clues when reading big numbers.
- Select 'use word cards' in the options menu. Drag a one-digit number word (for example 'five') into the lower box and invite the children to read out the number. Explain that all numbers that end in 5, such as 25 or 75, will have the word 'five' at the end. There is only one exception and it's a teen number.
- Ask the class to use their spy skills to find this teen number on the board - remind them that it will look and sound similar to 5. Ask them to whisper their answer to their partners (they must remember they are secret agents - who knows who may be listening!).
- Share suggestions and strategies before looking for other numbers.

Key questions

- *What clues did you look for?*
- *Are there any numbers that sound similar?*

Assessment for learning

Are the children able to read and find numbers up to 20?

Name _____ Date _____

Addition sentences

■ Write your own addition sentences in words and figures in the boxes below.

Words:

Figures:

Words:

Figures:

Words:

Figures:

Star Maths Tools ★ Year 1
PHOTOCOPIABLE